CINCHONA IN JAVA

The Story of Quinine

By

NORMAN TAYLOR

With an Introduction
BY PIETER HONIG

New York
GREENBERG : PUBLISHER

CINCHONA IN JAVA

Books by NORMAN TAYLOR

Flora of the Vicinity of New York

Botany: The Science of Plant Life

A Guide to the Wild Flowers

The Garden Dictionary

Cinchona In Java: The Story of Quinine

"MALARIA"
(*A Lyric of India*)

"He lurks among the reeds, beside the marsh,
    Red oleanders twisted in His hair,
His eyes are haggard and His lips are harsh,
    Upon His breast the bones show gaunt and bare.

"The green and stagnant waters lick His feet,
    And from their filmy, iridescent scum
Clouds of mosquitoes, gauzy in the heat,
    Rise with His gifts: Death and Delirium.

"His messengers: They bear the deadly taint
    On spangled wings aloft and far away,
Making thin music, strident and yet faint,
    From golden eve to silver break of day."

ACKNOWLEDGMENTS

Photographs in this book have come from the files of the Netherlands Information Bureau, the Cinchona Products Institute of New York, the Cinchona Institute of Amsterdam, Brown Brothers, and from a collection taken by the author in Bolivia.

Line drawings were made by Margaret Jervis, the head-pieces having been adapted from various examples of Indonesian art.

CONTENTS

Rice is the chief subsistence crop in Java.

INTRODUCTION

By Pieter Honig

AGRICULTURE in the Indies is of two kinds. The first and most important is directed wholly to the production of food and is largely in the hands of natives. The second comprises the export crops, of which sugar, tea, coffee, sisal, cinchona, cassava, tobacco, copra and rubber are the most important. Practically all the latter have been developed by Dutch, or at least foreign capital, and their successful culture has come from a welding of agricultural science with native labor. Why the latter has developed various horticultural skills of a pretty high order is no secret. Perhaps more than anything else, it is due to a land policy that fosters continuity of labor under social conditions which, in the tropics, is unique.

The allocation of land between subsistence and money crops has come after many years of study. Topographic and climatic features of Java, as we shall see presently, dictated some of those decisions. But a quickly growing population and the social implication of such rapid growth have often made it necessary to revise our allocations—not always in favor of producers of export crops.

Java, the most densely populated island on earth, has about the same area as the State of New York, but nearly four times the population. It has over 800 people to the square mile, the United States about 40. The feeding of nearly fifty million people on a tropical island not very different in size, shape and area from Cuba (population four million), has forced upon us an agricultural economy which differs from yours. Every inch of arable land fit for subsistence crops is cultivated with an intensity that would surprise most Americans. In an attempt to raise the utmost possible food from otherwise unproductive areas, some parts of the island, with only seasonal rainfall, have immense irrigation works costing millions of guilders.

As in any other agricultural venture we have had our failures, but crop failures, by a system of telegraphic reports seldom more than a few hours old, reach the Department of Agriculture in time to prevent famine. Disease-resistant or high yield seed is provided for next season's planting while the stricken community receives from the government food enough to carry on until the next harvest. No doubt the officials in charge of this very efficient system of crop reporting, the workers in the experiment stations and those charged with the rescue of temporarily deficient communities may be forgiven their boast that they have the most efficient information service in any tropical country. But the sober truth is that, without it, the government of the Netherlands Indies would have been derelict in its

HEVEA RUBBER PLANTATION

The Netherlands Indies produces about 40% of the world supply.

duty to the Javanese. No major famine has occcurred in Java within recent years.

Perhaps the most difficult hazard in keeping up the food supply is the great chain of mountains which forms the backbone of the island. Much of this range is too high for the cultivation of staple food crops. Also, on an island almost on the equator, there is great heat and much moisture over the greater part of the lowlands which makes for luxuriant growth, but also fosters plant diseases that need much attention.

While the struggle to maintain an adequate food supply does not come within the scope of this book, it has had profound effects upon the so-called "culture-crops" of which cinchona is one. Many years ago the government came to the conclusion that closer cooperation with the Javanese was socially and economically desirable for the best development of the Indies.

After much debate stretching over a long period of years, the liberals in Holland finally succeeded in passing an agrarian law that affects not only cinchona but all other export crops. Its object was the protection of the native population. One of its little known provisions was the stoppage of all revenue from the Indies to the home government in Holland. At agricultural experiment stations, prior to the war, a group of experts devoted their efforts to demonstration and instruction upon not only export crops but the ever present need to ensure the food supply. Unlike the system in the United States, our experiment stations are usually devoted to a single crop, two of the most important being wholly devoted to rubber and cinchona. The cinchona station has been in continuous existence since 1856.

Such liberal and often drastic changes in land management could not be accomplished over night. It is needless here to repeat all the political, economic and social movements that favored or fought the adoption of the agrarian law, for it took thirty years from 1870, when it began, until the final steps were taken in 1900. One of the first results was a considerable decrease in revenue. So acute did this become that the Netherlands Indies Government was forced to adopt a graduated national income tax in 1908. The burden of this was shouldered by corporate enterprise and residents from abroad, including the Dutch —scarcely at all by the native population.

The administration of the agrarian law was left to the government of the Indies. Its details would fill this book for it involves every native owner from the most lowly to hereditary princes. Only its main features are pertinent here and, of these, two are of chief significance:

The first and most important is the provision that no land can be owned by anyone who is not an actual native of the Indies. No Dutch or foreign capitalist is permitted to own any land for the production of crops, petroleum or tin. This applies also to Dutchmen who marry native women. As far as crop land is concerned it can only be leased upon terms to be explained presently.

All other unclaimed or disputed lands in Java were constituted as the public domain but none of this may be owned by or sold to a Dutchman or foreigner. Its use is wholly at the discretion of the Department of Civil Affairs, which may only lease it. This leasehold use of land in Java has, under existing conditions, done more for agriculture in the Indies than any other system. All rents from use of the public domain are paid to the government, while rents from agricultural land are paid to the native individuals or communities to whom the land belongs.

So far as agricultural development is concerned, and it has reached a high stage in Java, there are other factors of perhaps even more importance than who gets the rent. These are social, and inextricably tied up with the only terms upon which Dutch or foreign capital can get the right to use leased land. An illustration of its working is the following:

Assuming a Dutch stock company wants a tract of 5,000 acres of the public domain to establish a rubber or tea plantation, they can get it, after technical and financial requirements have satisfied the Department of Civil Affairs, only upon the following terms:

(a) At the corners of the property the company must put up a native village.

(b) Each family in the village must be provided with a house and land enough for simple subsistence crops, depending upon climate and elevation.

(c) Schools and public health necessities must be provided.

The effects of this are two-fold. If the stock company fails they do not leave behind them a destitute farming community. If the company succeeds, and many of them do, the workers are apt to live in such villages for generations. From such populations have come our most skilful workers in tropical agriculture.

Such a scheme makes for continuity of skilled labor matched by a continuity of expert supervision. It is the basis of the culture of export crops in the Indies, of which cinchona is merely one. In perennial cultures, like cinchona, leases may run 75 years, but there are many shorter leases for more ephemeral crops.

A policy such as this, notwithstanding its protection of the Javanese native, might in the humid tropics, easily invite disaster. Depletion of the land is guarded against by the insistence that all leaseholders in critical areas must plant and rotate the crops to conserve rather than destroy the fertility of the soil. It is the most priceless natural asset—without it no liberal or humanitarian improvement of the natives could be made to work.

Nowhere has the task been harder, for there is the perfectly natural conflict of interests as between the native population and the vital need for export crops. Only the latter and the industrial ventures can finance the services of transport, education and public health. Only the natives can provide the labor. The task has been to weld science and labor into a working combination, protecting those unable to protect themselves and taxing those able to bear it. The agrarian law is merely one of the features of that plan which has made the Indies what they are.

Having in large measure dispelled the fear of want from the native population of Java, it is interesting to record the comparatively small area of the country which has

SISAL PLANTATION

About 10% of the world supply comes from the Netherlands Indies.

actually been devoted to the main export crops. The most
recent figures are for 1939.

IMPORTANT EXPORT CROPS OF THE NETHERLANDS INDIES

In 1939

Crop	Area in Hectares	Number of Estates	Estate Production in long tons
Sugar	94,900	100	1,562,462
Hevea rubber	615,600	1199	198,087
Coffee	99,200	377	58,319
Tea	138,400	337	83,159
Tobacco	36,500	89	39,003
Cinchona bark	17,000	110	12,391
Oil palms	105,000	66	297,449

1 hectare—2.471 acres
1 long ton—1016 kilograms or 2240 pounds

These figures, except for sugar and cinchona bark, do
not reflect the total *exports* of these crops for some, like
tea and rubber, are not confined to estate production. Rubber, especially, is produced also by many native planters.

The total estate production of these major money crops
uses only 1,106,600 hectares or a little over two million
seven hundred thousand acres. The total area of Java
proper is just over 31 million acres, of which cinchona
culture occupies only about 42,000. There is, of course,
much virgin land, mostly in the mountains and in other
islands, which has not yet been brought under cultivation.
It is here where teak and other forest products are found.

* * * * *

[7]

It is difficult to describe the climate of the archipelago in general terms because local conditions vary greatly due to the influence of the high mountain ranges running across the island. Although the Indies form an equatorial belt, its climatic conditions are more equable than many other parts of the world because the island empire has a marine climate. Seasonally changing "monsoon" winds are more intense in the southern areas than in the northern islands, with the west monsoon accompanied by heavy rains which may last uninterruptedly for days and even for weeks. In Java the rainfall is less during the period from May to August, while the greatest precipitation generally occurs during December, January and February.

Java and Sumatra are amongst the most volcanic regions of the world. In Java the mountains exceeding 8000 feet in height are formed chiefly of quaternary rock, ultimately consisting of sand, ashes and dust. This formation disintegrates rapidly in the humid tropical climate, forming fertile agricultural soil which rotting vegetation helps to enrich. So many of the mountains are volcanic that eruptions have often interfered with the agricultural development. But one feature of Java, very favorable to cinchona culture, is the friable nature of soils of volcanic origin. This is particularly true in the Preanger Regency, in western Java, where most of the cinchona is grown. Much of the island is dominated by high mountains, culminating in Mt. Semeru, 12,057 feet high.

*　　*　　*　　*　　*

If there is something to be learned from the Netherlands Indies, it is that development is closely connected with a free exchange of experience, and with the recognition of the great value of every collaborator being given the opportunity to announce his views and have those views tested by experiments, the results of which are made available to the world.

What has proved to be a progressive improvement of agriculture in the Netherlands Indies is hoped to be reestablished there after the war. Although the exact day that the Indies will be freed of their invaders is still uncertain, there is no question in the minds of Dutchmen and Indonesians that, in co-operation with other democratic nations, they will find the answer to their destiny by helping to produce more of the world's needs better than ever before.

1 THE TRAGEDY OF MALARIA

AMONG the unsolved mysteries of medicine is the origin of malaria. No disease has killed so many, and its victims even today are numbered by the hundreds of millions. Where and how it started no one surely knows— perhaps we inherited it from our simian ancestors. For monkey malaria is still the nearest thing to the scourge of human malaria.

Wherever it started, malaria soon began its ravages. From the dawn of history down to yesterday it has shifted populations, made huge regions all but uninhabitable, and often switched the currents of history. How much the fall of Greece and Rome was due to malaria may be left to the different schools of historians, but the abandonment of the Roman Campagna in the sixteenth century was wholly due to it. In fact Missiroli has published a chart of the waves of malaria in Italy which shows virulent outbreaks in the third and fourth centuries B.C. and in the 6th, 7th, 11th, 12th, and 18th and 19th centuries of

Prospecting for new *Cinchona* sites in the Preanger Regency of western Java.

our era. It was not for nothing that Livy and Cicero described Rome as "the pestilential city"; and one section of it, even in modern times, is called "The Vale of Hell."

Similar charts, if the data were available, could no

MADONNA OF THE FEVER
From a 14th-century painting in the Crypt of Saint Peter's at Rome.

doubt be made for every region where malaria has become established.

Such charts (for Greece, Macedonia or especially Africa) would be of absorbing interest to modern epidemiologists. The latter, long called the "Dark Continent," is also known as the "Malarious Continent," as Sir Ronald Ross called it. He worked there for some years and could never get over the immensity of the malarial prob-

[11]

lem. He wrote: "For centuries the successive waves of civilization which have flooded and fertilized Europe and America, have broken themselves in vain upon its shores."

Seventeen of the southern states in the United States are afflicted with it, while in most tropical regions it is endemic. Whether it was found in the New World before Columbus, is still a disputed point. Its ravages in the United States have been estimated to cost half a billion dollars annually.

The untold suffering over the centuries seems all the more tragic because neither the cause nor cure of malaria were even suspected. Sometimes it ruined a military campaign by the killing of such a general as Alexander the Great, and Caesar was plagued by it. It also cut off the life of an artist like Albrecht Dürer. Neither the great nor the lowly were safe, and for over three thousand years malaria was our greatest scourge.

While it is thus historically easy to prove the devastation of malaria, and to lament the futile centuries of helplessness, science is loath to doze in the past. And it is to science that the world turned for hope of the future. At the first dawn of hope it was, however, not science but the church which played the chief role. For at Lima, Peru, about 1630, came the news that a cure for malaria had finally been found by some Jesuit priests. To the malaria-stricken Old World no song of Inca gold was so welcome as this new-found bark of the Cinchona tree. Legends grew up around it, most of them false, but they still have a romantic appeal.

There followed, for nearly two hundred years, a huge employment of the bark as a cure for malaria without any notion of the constituents of it. Science found the

[12]

answer in the isolation of quinine by a couple of French chemists in 1820. But the cause of malaria was still in the stage where malaria (bad air) expressed the idea that the disease was caused only by the noxious evaporation from swamps.

Ancient fresco from the hospital of Santo Spirito, Rome. It depicts Cardinal Juan de Lugo giving cinchona to malaria sufferers. Its inscription reads: "The purple-clad father comforts the sick in this building with the fever bark of Lima."

Science finally disproved the marsh theory of malaria, isolated the plasmodium that causes it and proved that it can only be carried by anopheline mosquitoes. Why such triumphs did not end malaria has surprised many who naturally wonder just what was the value of these discoveries. One of the scientists, after his discovery of the mosquito-born nature of malaria, had the only true answer —the ever present menace of the anopheles mosquito. It is world-wide in all warm regions, and in many others with warm summers.

The discovery of cinchona bark and the ultimate isolation of quinine were landmarks scarcely less important than the technicalities of malaria transmittal. Scientific dicta are apt to be forgotten by a busy world, but no one could afford to ignore quinine once its efficacy was established. Its acceptance is best expressed in the annual consumption of it. In normal times this ranges from about 650 to 750 tons yearly. In 1941 (the last year before the fall of Java) it was 1017 tons, due to the much increased need for it by a world at war.

The story of quinine, which is the main purpose of this book, is thus scarcely three hundred years old—a mere episode in the long history of malaria. But into the *Cinchona* story there has been woven a fabric of many colors. The fact that quinine provided the only known cure for the most serious disease on earth was bound to have many ramifications, both medical and commercial. How should it be used? How much did the world need? A hundred other questions were to arise. Some were settled by science, some by commerce, a few by charlatans, and as in all human enterprise there was a fair mixture of idealism and greed.

This confusion of motives is still with us. Two of the greatest colonial empires in the world have striven to supply themselves and the rest of mankind with this indispensable drug. One of them has so far surpassed all others that the story of *Cinchona* in Java stands almost alone in man's attempt to wring from nature a cure for one of nature's greatest plagues.

[14]

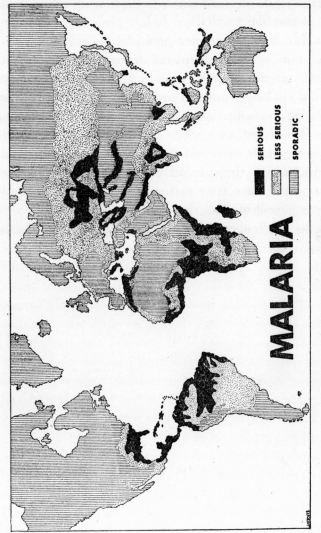

MALARIA

SERIOUS
LESS SERIOUS
SPORADIC

World's Malaria Regions.

The struggle has not been easy. Popular delusions would have it that the tropics are lush regions where planting inevitably leads to rich and often fantastic harvests with little or no effort. Experienced foresters and experts in tropical agriculture know better. While nature supplies the plant, a climate, a soil and perhaps a few imponderables, man must do his bit. Sometimes the plant must be changed, the soil modified, or a whole technique of growth drastically revised. Experts and their helpers, from geneticists and chemists to the simplest native, must work together. In Java they have done so for more than seventy years. It is no accident that cinchona cultivation has become what the Dutch once thought it might be—"A pearl in the Crown of the Netherlands."

2 THE CAUSE OF IT

To use quinine without some idea of the target at
which it is aimed is to employ a "shot-gun" therapy
that rightly disturbs the medical profession. It therefore
seems appropriate to include in a book on *Cinchona* in
Java, a brief account of just what malaria is. The basic
story behind the cause of malaria is chiefly concerned
with the triple life of a microscopic organism, the existence of which was never suspected until November 6,
1880. Prior to that the cause of malaria was as unknown
to medicine as to its millions of victims.

The idea that marshes and malaria were somehow connected had persisted for centuries, in fact ever since Varro,
a Roman gentleman-farmer, first suspected it. Just before
the birth of Christ he wrote what amounts to the first
treatise on country life, *De re rustica,* in which he says of
malaria "that in marshes there are animals too small to be
seen, but which enter the mouth and nose and cause
troublesome diseases." There are other but more apoch-

ryphal references to the marsh theory of malaria which went under a variety of names. An Italian, Torti (1658-1741), is supposed to have finally coined the term *malaria*, and thereby perpetuated in the name of the disease all the erroneous notions that it was really bad air (*mal aire*) that caused it. Hugh Walpole knew the term in 1740, and it may antedate this.

Its real cause is a microscopic protozoan to which the generic name *Plasmodium* was applied soon after the first one was demonstrated in the red blood corpuscle of a man. That discovery, at Constantine, Algeria, on November 6, 1880, was made by a young French Army doctor, Charles Louis Alphonse Laveran, then only 25 years old. If the Nobel prizes had existed then, Laveran should have had one, for he was the first to throw the clear light of demonstrated science upon the long darkness of malaria.

Plasmodium, which is neither a fungus nor a bacterium, is a uni-cellular organism not so distantly related to amoeba. In one stage of its life history it multiplies asexually by simple division and at an appalling rate. In a severe case of malaria, millions of plasmodia may be found in the blood stream where they quite literally destroy the red blood corpuscles. Some doctors have even written rather colorfully of them as "exploding" the red blood cells. If too many are destroyed the patient inevitably dies.

Since Laveran discovered the first one, several other species of plasmodia, and also varieties of these species have been found. There are, today, *Plasmodium* experts who devote most of their time to studying the relationship and ramifications of this powerful protozoan which in spite

CHARLES LOUIS ALPHONSE LAVERAN (1845-1922)
First to discover *Plasmodium* in the blood stream of a malaria
patient, November 6, 1880.

of its microscopic size has taken more lives than all the wars of history.

While it may seem fruitless to delve too deeply into the secrets of *Plasmodium*, it is a fact that the discovery of the first one did not quite solve all the riddle of malaria. Theophrastus, Galen and many others recognized that

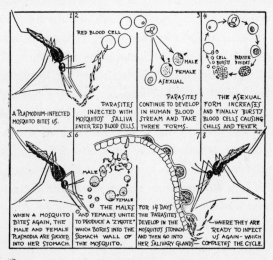

Life history of *Plasmodium* and how it perpetuates malaria.

malaria was not just malaria, but of several divergent forms. These differed in the number of days between chills and fever, in their virulence and most of all in their mortality. It is now known that these different sorts of malaria are caused by the various species and varieties of *Plasmodium*. These need not detain us, for all agree in a fact which can scarcely be emphasized enough, for upon it depends the transmittal of malaria.

[19]

It is obvious that the discovery of a single species of *Plasmodium* in the blood stream of a man tells us nothing of how one gets malaria. It might explain why some Italian cities treated it like the plague—by headlong flight, leaving the poor and destitute to die "in their own stench."

Few discoveries reveal enough, and Laveran's was a good example. Since his day it is known that *Plasmodium* leads a triple life: two stages in man and the third in some species of the *Anopheles* mosquito. Laveran found only one stage and is rightly put among the immortals. Another immortal who received the Nobel prize for his part in unrolling the hidden scroll of malaria, was Sir Ronald Ross.

Working in malaria-infected India, where he was born, this quiet English doctor first demonstrated the malaria parasite in the stomach of a mosquito. The implications were staggering and Ross knew it, for he had hit upon the method of how *Plasmodium* was carried from man to man. The culprit was an anopheles mosquito, but he attached no importance to that. Enough that this devout doctor (he wrote a religious poem the evening of his discovery) had for the first time demonstrated the mechanism of the transmission of malaria. It was at Begumpet, Secunderabad, India, on August 25, 1897, and a marble tablet marks the house to this day. A few months later, Giovanni Battista Grassi, an Italian zoologist, proved that the *Anopheles* was the only mosquito that could carry plasmodia from man to man.

This trio of scientists, the French Laveran, the British Ross and the Italian Grassi, set the stage for our understanding of the triple life-history of plasmodium, the true

SIR RONALD ROSS (1867-1932)

First to discover *Plasmodium* in the stomach of a mosquito, August 25, 1897.

GIOVANNI BATTISTA GRASSI (1854-1925)

First to discover it is only the *Anopheles* mosquito that carries the parasite of malaria, 1898.

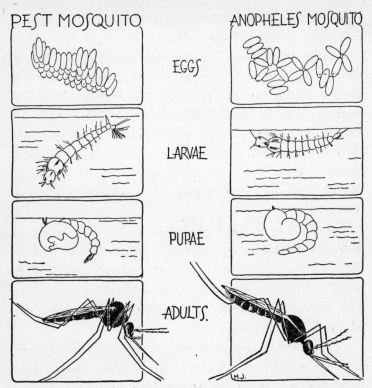

PEST MOSQUITO   ANOPHELES MOSQUITO

EGGS

LARVAE

PUPAE

ADULTS.

Life history of the pest mosquito (*left*) and the *Anopheles* mosquito (*right*). The malaria culprit mostly flies at night, buzzes faintly, and only the female carries the malaria parasite. The pest mosquito carries no malaria.

cause of malaria, and the transmittal of the disease by mosquitoes. And Ross, the discoverer of the latter fact, also insisted that for the first time we could then understand the rationale of quinine administration as the cure for malaria.

Plasmodium, like any other animal, must feed and find some method of reproduction. It is precisely in performing

[21]

these vital functions that the organism throws off human malaria—as a sort of by-product.

To understand how, it is necessary to find the beginning, only to discover that the beginning is a bit nebulous and the end all but eternal. For we are not dealing with a true start that can be pegged down as an engineer starts his "point of beginning"—but with a never ending and continuous cycle. And so it has been without respite for thousands of years. This vicious circle involves two stages of the plasmodium's life history in man and one in the mosquito.

It appears to be a matter of considerable indifference to plasmodium where we start our story, because, to it, man is a mere incident—a sort of necessary seed bed. It needs our red blood, and so, quite arbitrarily, let us start with the moment when a plasmodium-laden *Anopheles* mosquito first bites us.

At this moment the mosquito is carrying in its salivary glands a sexless, uni-cellular stage of plasmodium—provided that it is an anopheles mosquito, of the female sex, bent upon what the zoologists call somewhat realistically, a "blood meal." In the process of sucking our blood the mosquito quite inadvertently leaves behind a few of these potentially dangerous plasmodia.

Beyond the irritation of the bite we are quite unconscious that anything else has happened, although the few plasmodia are already in our blood stream and destined to make much mischief. At this stage and for several days thereafter quinine, nor any known drug, is completely ineffective, either to kill them or retard their inevitable

[22]

destiny which is to cause the soon impending outbreak of what we call malaria.

Actually, we have really had malaria, or the potentiality for developing it, from the moment of the infective bite of the mosquito. Hence, the doctor's preference for "clinical malaria" as a term to define only the actual stages of chills and fever. It is more precise than the too inclusive *malaria* and will be so used hereafter.

This first, pre-clinical stage of malaria may last for 9-15 days, depending partly upon one's condition and partly upon the species of *Plasmodium* carried by the mosquito.

During this period, plasmodia are multiplying rapidly, quietly infesting blood corpuscles until the time when clinical malaria is ready to flare up. It is at this stage that quinine administration is begun, without any notion, even yet, as to just what quinine does to plasmodium if, indeed, it works directly upon the organism at all. Quinine and malaria have been so long associated that most people have used it as a cure, without stopping to inquire how it works.

While this world-wide use of the drug may be unscientific, its effectiveness, while wholly empiric, has raised quinine to the rank of one of the few real specifics known to medicine.

During the bout of clinical malaria, the plasmodium splits off into two forms. One is still asexual and can cause a relapse unless aborted by therapy or prevented by something akin to immunity which the fortunate few can set up. Some of these are driven into the bone marrow or spleen, and quite literally hide, poised for a fresh attack whenever adverse conditions invite them into the blood stream.

[23]

It is this fact that makes malaria a naturally relapsing disease.

The balance of the plasmodia still left in the blood stream after clinical malaria has subsided, are incomparably the most important in the world picture of malaria. Known as gametocytes, they can never cause a relapse into clinical malaria, although they may live in one's blood stream about a month after clinical malaria has subsided.

These gametocytes are the unmated male and female form of *Plasmodium* as yet quite virgin. But of far more importance is the fact that it is only at this stage that a mosquito can carry on the last of the triple stages in the life history of *Plasmodium* and ensure the perpetuation of malaria.

The mosquito carries human blood loaded with gametocytes, and these, in the stomach of a mosquito, complete the sexual act. From that union comes ultimately the stage of the plasmodium mentioned above as the "starting" point of malaria. (See the chart, page 19.)

It is easy to see now that far from being a starting point, it is merely a small fraction of a circle comprising the amazing set of apparently fortuitous circumstances that make up the life history of *Plasmodium*. Man, the mosquito, and malaria are mere incidents in the life history of an organism that needs our blood for food, uses the stomach of a mosquito to complete its sex life, and in the process causes the most devastating disease known to science. The yearly record of cases is supposed to be 800,000,000 and the annual deaths are probably more than 3,000,000.

These bare outlines of life history may vary a little in

the different species of *Plasmodium,* but such differences are of interest chiefly to the experts. Three main species are of practical importance: *P. vivax* which causes benign tertian malaria; *P. falciparum,* the source of malignant tertian malaria and *P. malariae* which is responsible for quartan malaria.

MALARIA "CONTROL"

The eradication of malaria is still little more than a pious hope. For it would involve the destruction either of all mosquitoes or of mankind. There is no other way of breaking the cyclic life of *Plasmodium* except by eliminating one of its vital hosts. While man is a mere incident to the malarial organism, we still seem, in spite of war, to cherish enough instinct for survival to focus attention on some other phases of the malaria problem, than that suggested by the young student: "Why not eliminate man?" That decision has profound effects upon medical theory, upon philanthropic and public health efforts and upon the planting of the cinchona tree in the mountains of Java— the only source of quinine beyond a negligible fraction from Latin America and India.

Eradication of malaria being impossible, the next step was the setting up of machinery to attempt to *control* malaria. This far more practical viewpoint recognized the futility of attempting to eradicate either the *Plasmodium* or the mosquito. The International Health Division of the Rockefeller Foundation established malaria control units all over the world. They studied the life history of *Anopheles* and all that this implies in the transmission of malaria, the eradication of mosquitoes in areas of dense population, and their control by ditching or spreading of larvicides.

Perhaps the most notable of attempts to control mosquitoes was the almost complete eradication of *Anopheles gambiae,* a particularly virulent type of mosquito accidentally introduced into northeastern Brazil from Africa. Before control was started, malaria from this mosquito claimed thousands of victims and resulted in an appalling number of deaths. The campaign cost over two million dollars and more than two thousand trained workers were used in this most ambitious attempt to stop malaria by the eradication of all mosquitoes in an area of over 12,000 square miles. Recently (November 1943), *Anopheles gambiae* has turned up again in Natal, Brazil.

Such a spectacular triumph did not allay the scepticism found among many competent observers that there was something more to malaria control than the eradication of mosquitoes. How could one explain that there are anopheline mosquitoes over much of Europe and North America, while malaria is restricted by some other and quite unknown factor to special regions? As Hackett puts it, such a fact "creates a lively scepticism as to the fundamental validity of the thesis that malaria can actually be controlled by reducing the numbers of anopheline mosquitoes."

Some malariologists have specialized upon the control of the parasite in man, which can only be done by drugs, and until recently this meant only the administration of quinine. Their theory was that it is better to cure sick people than to spend too much time on trying to break the life cycle of *Plasmodium*, whether by drainage, screening, or other methods of mosquito control.

A more reasonable attitude, for the layman, and the only justifiable one, is to leave this attack upon malaria to the experts. The problem is so huge that only some well co-ordinated plan carried out by those trained for it is at all likely to succeed. There have been many failures, some great successes, the cost is enormous and there are still some technical points in dispute.

Ever since Ross discovered the mechanism of malaria transmission, the attempt to control it by drugs has put upon the planters of cinchona a responsibility that can scarcely be exaggerated. The Java planters, who grow a tree that must be destroyed to yield its crop of quinine-yielding bark, were faced with the problem of calculating how much to grow. The real harvest comes only after years of expensive culture, for cinchona is a difficult tree to keep up to its maximum yield of quinine. There are, too, many species of *Cinchona*, some quite worthless. How the Dutch planters conquered the hazards and provided the world with quinine is a story of tropical agriculture almost without parallel in the history of such ventures.

3   DISCOVERY OF CINCHONA

For twelve hundred miles along the Eastern slopes of the Andes, from Bolivia to Colombia and even extending into a corner of Venezuela, lies the genus *Cinchona*. Never much below 2,500 feet these shrubs and trees may range up to elevations of 9,000 or even 10,000 feet. All of them grow in regions of abundant rainfall and some are as near the frost line as tropical trees can be expected to grow.

Only a few of them are of the slightest interest as far as the production of quinine is concerned, and even these have been wholly supplanted by varieties that originated in Java long after the tree was taken from South America to that island. A little quinine, but not enough for local needs, is now produced in most of the countries where the tree grows. This is practically all produced under government auspices and so cannot be compared with commercially produced Java bark.

Long before quinine was isolated for the first time in

1820 there had developed an enormous trade in wild cinchona bark, crude infusions of which were the only means of treating malaria before that time. Exploitation on a tremendous scale was rampant. Governmental and private bark monopolies were created and destroyed, notably in Peru and Bolivia, and for two hundred years the cascilleros or bark gatherers were scouring the forests for new sources of cinchona bark.

From the earliest days most of these bark strippers were Indians, but one of the most remarkable features of cinchona history is the fact that the Incas knew nothing of its value, the origin of which has led to romantic tales and endless confusion both among the botanists and pharmacologists.

Pizarro completed the conquest of Peru (then far more extensive than now) in 1537, leaving many records, but no mention of *quina*, the Peruvian vernacular for cinchona. The son of one of his captains, Gracilasso de la Vega, whose mother was the daughter of an Inca noble, subsequently wrote his "Royal Commentaries on the Incas." The young Gracilasso, who mentions many native remedies, and gives a good description of the potato, does not mention cinchona, nor does Acosta, one of the great Spanish friars who wrote on the natural history of the new empire of Spain. Their failure to mention cinchona would not of itself prove that the tree was unknown to the Incas, but the lack of it in any of their pharmacopoeias, faithfully translated by the Spaniards, seems to justify the verdict of history that cinchona was unknown to the Incas.

That failure makes all the more extraordinary the announcement, about a hundred years later, that came from

Lima. Long credited to the Countess of Chinchon, the fact appears to be that Jesuit priests at Lima, about 1630, were the ones who first discovered the anti-malarial value of *Cinchona* bark. The authenticity of this appears to be unquestioned, but the Countess of Chinchon legend will no doubt persist, if for nothing else but for the fact that the tree was subsequently named in her honor. The facts in the case are as follows:

The Countess of Chinchon, the wife of the Spanish Viceroy, was supposed to have been stricken with malaria in Lima in 1630 and snatched from the verge of the grave by the timely intervention of adequate potions of the bark of quina. So grateful was the lady that the ground-up bark was promptly christened Countess' Powder and she is credited with introducing it to malaria-stricken Spain and Italy. It is a pretty legend, swallowed by Linnaeus, who named the trees *Cinchona* * in her honor, and by everyone else until November, 1941.

The three-hundred year old canard was finally exploded by A. W. Haggis in *The Bulletin of the History of Medicine* for October and November, 1941, published at Johns Hopkins University. This proves that the Countess never had malaria, that her husband often did, but that even for the Viceroy there was no cure by cinchona bark, for no one at Lima then knew anything about it. Nor did the Countess ever take it to Europe for she died on her way home, as is proved by the Archives of Franciscan Friars at Lima, who wrote:

---

* Linnaeus dropped an "h" in naming *Cinchona* for the Countess of Chinchon. According to the rules of botanical nomenclature his mistake must be perpetuated, notwithstanding the subsequent confusion in spelling.

[30]

Eighty years after the discovery of quinine by Pelletier and Caventou the people of France erected this statue to their memory on the Boulevard St. Michel, Paris.

"By these presents let it be known unto you how, on the 14th January of this year 1641, in the City of Carthagena of the Continent of this Kingdom, Our Lord gathered unto Himself, Donna Francisca Henriquez de Ribera, Countess of Chinchon and a patronness of our Holy religion."

This would seem to dispose of the Countess of Chinchon legend but tells us nothing as to who first took cinchona bark to Europe, nor when. It is first mentioned in European medical literature by a Belgian, Herman van der Heyden, in his *Discours et Advis sur les Flus de Ventre Doloureux*, published at Antwerp in 1643. Its value must have been known then, and there the early history of cinchona must rest, awaiting further research.

It would be pleasant to follow the reception of cinchona bark in Europe, for it comprises by far the most colorful episode in the all but incredible history of quinine. Kings, queens, princes, cardinals, the Jesuits, even the Pope jostle doctors, apothecaries, the great Sydenham and the most fabulous of quacks (Robert Talbor). Ecclesiastical intrigues, fierce controversies by the medical profession, bitter fights among rival owners of cinchona nostrums followed each other with amazing speed and rancour. The final inclusion of Peruvian bark, for the first time, in the British Pharmacopoeia of 1677, while it did not put a stop to this turmoil, at least put cinchona bark in the class of respectable remedies.

The effect of all this upon South America was deplorable, ultimately leading to the extinction of its large trade in cinchona and finally forcing the British and Dutch to attempt cultivation of the tree. Competent botanists, sent out by worried governments, warned again and again that such ruthless cutting of cinchona trees could only lead to disaster. But greed and incompetence won the day aided not a little by the very scientists who most wished to help.

Until the isolation of quinine there was no way of telling the therapeutic effectiveness of any bark sample except by trial and error. Most of the barks contained,

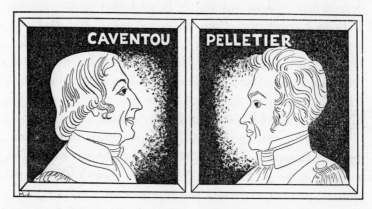

Joseph B. Caventou (1795-1877), Joseph Pelletier (1788-1842). They isolated quinine from cinchona bark, for the first time, in a laboratory at Paris on September 11, 1820. Caventou was 25 years old and Pelletier 32.

besides quinine—quinidine, cinchonine and cinchonidine, none of which was even suspected throughout the most ruthless period of exploitation.

The ignorance of its constituents, until after 1820, made the botany and pharmacology of *Cinchona* a fertile field. Distinguished experts saw fancied differences and created species upon them. Great schools of thought fought over the relative merits of red, yellow, Loxa, crown, and a dozen other varieties of bark. It all seems academic now and quite futile, but large professional and financial interests were involved—manufacturers, chemists, and botanists, with a fair sprinkling of native incompetence.

After the isolation of quinine, bark collecting became for the first time a measurably effective procedure. Bark was bought upon the content of quinine sulfate. It then became doubly clear that the whole scheme before this had been wholly futile, for most of the barks contained little or no quinine. Those that did, provided what would today be considered a pitifully small amount of quinine sulfate.

Meanwhile the world's population was increasing and with it the malaria hazard. Tropical colonization grew apace and it became obvious that South America would never keep up with the world demand for quinine. Many distinguished men realized this and it is now idle to detail their repeated warnings. Even the Jesuits at Lima, back in 1640, had ordered that for every tree cut down a new one was to be planted. No one took any notice and the unregulated scramble for bark went on almost unheeded. La Condamine and his botanical colleague Jussieu, Weddell, Mutis, Triana, Humboldt and Bonpland, Ruis and Pavon and in later years, Rusby—all visited the *Cinchona* regions and told the same tale. Antonio Ulloa, an accurate chronicler, put it in a nutshell when he wrote as far back as 1735: "Though the trees are numerous, they have an end."

More than a hundred years later (in 1848), Weddell brought some seeds of *Cinchona calisaya* from Bolivia to Paris. Some were germinated in the Jardin des Plantes, others in the garden of the Horticultural Society of London. These, the first *Cinchona* plants ever to be grown in

Europe, were ultimately sent to Algiers and Java. It was the first experimental groping after the idea that the world must look elsewhere than to South America for its quinine. Both plantings were a failure, but both presaged a new chapter in the story of cinchona. For a hundred and fifty years, La Paz had been the cinchona capital of the world. Years later that distinction was to fall upon a mountain town in Java.

4   BRITISH AND DUTCH ATTEMPTS

S o obvious had it finally become that South American
bark production would not keep pace with world
demand, that England and Holland determined to bring
Cinchona from the New World and cultivate it in the Old.
Public men in both countries had long urged this but governmental apathy had completely frustrated any real attempts to accomplish it.

But far-sighted men would not let the issue die and
urged, in season and out, that something must be done. At
last something was and its effects have had a profound
influence upon the East Indian possessions of both countries. The first practical step was taken by the Dutch.

Many experienced Dutch botanists and horticulturists
had petitioned the government in Java and Holland for
years with the idea that cinchona cultivation in the
Netherlands Indies would be a success. But no one paid
much attention even to the pleadings of such scientists as
deVogel, Vrolik, Blume, Mulder, de Vriese or Miquel.
At last the Minister for the Colonies, C. F. Pahud, whose
name should be imperishable in Dutch history, made the

first serious move in 1852 to accomplish what so many had urged.

The motive was purely humanitarian. Governor-General Rochussen of the Netherlands Indies who furthered the effort, stated plainly what the Dutch were after:

"The eyes of Europe are fixed upon this enterprise which interests it in the highest degree; for it is, so to speak, to procure for the sick, the means of life, and to procure it at a cost which will not exceed his means. This is no common speculation, it is a humanitarian work that the Dutch government has undertaken, ..."

Years later, on February 14, 1864, a decree of the Netherlands East Indies Government stated that "The culture of *Cinchona* must not be regarded in any aspect as a financial speculation." There was little but outgo and faith to motivate the Dutch when it was at last settled that J. C. Hasskarl, of the Buitenzorg Botanical Garden, was to be sent to South America to collect seeds and plants of *Cinchona*.

Hasskarl was in many ways a remarkable man, for he was willing to embark upon a dangerous and difficult mission without any special training in *Cinchona* cultivation, as no one really knew anything about it at that time. Everyone did know that the different South American countries were opposed to the exportation of seeds or plants of *Cinchona* for fear they would lose their monopoly of the bark trade. Furthermore, Hasskarl's trip was almost ruined before he started, by an "accident." Upon his arrival in Holland for last-minute instructions from his government, it was discovered that his mission had been prematurely publicised by the German daily *Hamburgische Corre-spondent*. This would practically have prevented his landing in any South American country. With characteristic efficiency he did not abandon his plans, as some government officials suggested, but secured passports under the assumed name of J. K. Müller, and sailed from The Hague on December 4, 1852.

If the Hasskarl expedition had been a success it would perhaps be worth tracing his perilous route through the mountains of Peru and Bolivia where he worked with all the energy and foresight at his command. He picked up many of the species and varieties of *Cinchona* over the identity of which Weddell and his colleagues had been quarrelling for years. In the light of modern knowledge practically all of them were worthless, but no one knew it then.

Hasskarl had already sent to Java thousands of seeds of these dubious varieties, among the best of which was *Cinchona calisaya*. Finally he petitioned the government to put a warship at his disposal, which was granted, and he sailed from Callao, Peru, for Java on the "Prins Frederik Hendrik" (Captain van Braam Houckgeest) at the end of August, 1854, with 500 plants of *C. calisaya* and a large quantity of seeds.

Upon his arrival at Batavia on December 13, 1854, the transit by sea had killed all but 75 of his plants, but these were immediately sent to Tjibodas on the eastern slopes of the Gedeh mountains, at an elevation of just over 4,500 feet. It turned out to be an unfortunate site, for as pointed out by Junghuhn, it was too low in elevation, too windy and exposed, and was then in constant danger from the eruption of a neighboring volcano.*

In spite of the comparative failure of the Hasskarl mission, he had acquired first hand knowledge of *Cinchona* in its natural habitat and it is not surprising that the Dutch government put him in charge of all *Cinchona* culture in Java. Other persons were not slow to suggest what they supposed were better methods, and there existed for some time the inevitable conflicts of opinion, and not always urbane debate, on the whole venture. In the light of what was at stake and what happened after, it is now quite idle to relate these growing pains of an infant industry. Perhaps it gives one a better perspective to recount other Dutch attempts to supplement the Hasskarl collection.

Holland was fortunate in having as Consul General at La Paz, Bolivia, an intelligent official who followed the instructions of his government with fidelity and energy. This was C. N. Schuhkraft, who literally bombarded Java with hundreds of thousands of seeds of *Cinchona* during many years. Other seeds sent in by various collectors were either sent to Java direct or germinated in Holland and trans-shipped as living plants. The fate of the latter was precarious in the extreme. Complete failure or only partial success became so common that only Dutch pertinacity would have survived such setbacks. Time after time one reads of 10 or sometimes only two plants surviving the sea voyage which began with hundreds of vigorous seedlings. Perhaps the most disheartening of these efforts was the

* One of the hazards of cinchona culture in Java, during this period, was the occasional destruction of nursery seedlings by a wandering rhinoceros.

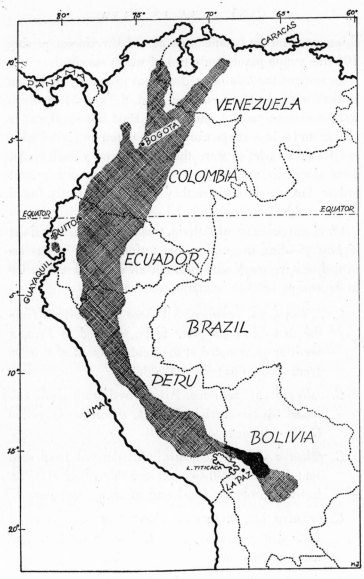

CINCHONA REGIONS OF SOUTH AMERICA
The best wild barks came, and still come, from Bolivia.

[39]

shipment from the botanical garden of Utrecht comprising
106 fine young plants, only two of which survived.

In spite of these failures, Java was gradually becoming
stocked with plants raised from seed, the arrival of which
was pretty continuous from 1854 to 1864. Hasskarl was in
charge and it is perhaps worth while to put on record what
species and varieties were then considered valuable. All
have since disappeared, sometimes due to government
orders, but mostly because they were subsequently found
to be worthless.

Cinchona calisaya, of Bolivia, was always considered the
highest yielding in quinine, but unfortunately it was assumed to have many varieties, not all of equal worth. Up
to the end of 1863 the situation was as follows:

C. calisaya var. *javanica.* All these were derived from
the first *Cinchona* plant to be received in Java, a
seedling germinated at the Leiden Botanical Garden
from seed collected by Weddell.

C. calisaya var. *javanica.* All derived from seeds collected by Hasskarl in Bolivia, subsequently called
C. hasskarliana.

C. calisaya var. *"Schuhkraft."* All derived from seed
sent in by Consul-General Schuhkraft of La Paz,
Bolivia, probably consisting of many varieties.

C. calisaya var. *anglica.* Derived from seed received
from British India, where cinchona plantations had
already been started.

In addition to these there were a dozen or so "species," not
one of which is grown in Java today, but they, with the ones

listed above, were to complicate enormously the problem in the future, due to the great tendency of *Cinchona* to hybridize.

The magnitude of the Dutch mistake, understandable in a pioneer venture, is best expressed in their figures of planting material at the end of 1863:

Seeds not yet germinated	208,322
Plants in nurseries	612,770
Plants in permanent sites	539,040

To obtain such a result implied a huge expenditure of money and the clearing of thousands of acres of mountainous jungle. But what had really been accomplished? Dr. M. Kerbosch, who contributed ultimately to final success, put it, in 1930, with typical Dutch realism: "The preservation of *Cinchona* from extermination, had to a certain extent been attained, but it did not appear as if its cultivation in Java would prove to be an economic success. . . ."

But what of the government of the Netherlands Indies? What answer could such a government make in 1863 to a hardheaded practical people whose taxes were being absorbed for a project that was an obvious failure. The rival claims of coffee, tea, sugar and other profitable crops (it was before the days of sisal or rubber in Java) were hard to answer by a government on the defensive. But somehow the storm was weathered, cultivation was continued in spite of the fact that no Dutchman dreamed that just around the corner, the most remarkable exploit in the long history of *Cinchona* was about to burst upon them.

[41]

BRITISH EFFORTS

While all this had been happening in Holland and Java, the watchful British had by no means been asleep. Years before Hasskarl's trip, the bringing of *Cinchona* to India had been a topic of conversation among botanists in London and occasionally it reached the more august ears of government officials. Nothing was done, however, until Clements R. Markham finally convinced the government that something must be done and he was the man to do it. It is impossible at this time to speculate whether the British effort would have succeeded if someone else had been put in charge. By training Markham was neither a botanist nor a horticulturist, although he proposed to do a most difficult job requiring just these attributes.

Interested in archaeology and geography, with considerable knowledge of South America, and facility in some Peruvian dialects and Spanish, he proposed to overcome his obvious technical deficiencies by taking along botanists and horticulturists.

This was agreed to by the British government and he started to South America upon the most ambitious plan to conquer *Cinchona* ever devised. He left England in December 1859, having as fellow workers John Weir, a young gardener, who went with Markham to the *C. calisaya* region of Bolivia; Dr. Richard Spruce, a noted botanist, who was to explore *Cinchona* in Ecuador with the assistance of Robert Cross, a Scotch gardener; and a Mr. Pritchett, who took over the Peruvian section of the enterprise.

The journeys of these different workers are all recorded in Markham's *Peruvian Bark,* published in 1880, in the preface to which he says that his "introduction of Peruvian bark trees into British India and Ceylon, is now an assured success." Perhaps the best commentary on this is the fact that 20 years later more than a million trees of Markham's *Cinchona* in Ceylon were cut down because their culture was unprofitable. And in 1943, quinine was still so desperately needed in India that the government was offering a bounty if private planters would again start *Cinchona* plantations, most of which had been abandoned years ago.

It is as useless to detail the British failure as to ridicule the preposterous claims of Markham, for the British Indian cinchona muddle has been a major tragedy. Malaria is such a critical public health matter that for years the responsible doctors have been clamoring for more and better government cinchona plantations. These have been continued, at a loss, ever since Markham's day. Only so, can cinchona febrifuge, and more recently, totaquina, be supplied to the millions of malaria victims. The extraction of quinine sulfate is so low that the British have been obliged to supplement their supplies by heavy importations of both quinine and bark from Java.

The British experience is thus not unlike that of the earliest Dutch attempt. Both failed because the species secured did not yield enough quinine to make it worth growing them. But in India, with characteristic British tenacity, the government obstinately clung to species and methods long proved disadvantageous. This is all the more extraordinary for there was the most friendly interchange of plants, seeds and methods between Madras and Java.

[43]

And the successive directors of both enterprises made frequent visits to their colleagues. Some of this interchange of ideas and plants has had a profound effect upon the future of cinchona culture in both regions.

Java, soon after these early attempts of the Dutch and British, was destined to start on that course which led to its becoming the world source of quinine.

5   CINCHONA IN JAVA:
      THE FORMATIVE YEARS

~~~~~~

A T THE end of Chapter IV we left the Dutch in the some-
      what dubious position of persisting in an acknowl-
edged failure. Hostile critics were keen to abandon the
whole enterprise, the personnel was not exactly happy,
and the government stuck to its determination only with
considerable difficulty.

No private planter in his right mind would, in 1864, nor
for years afterwards, look at cinchona. There was, or appeared to be, no hope of profit in the venture. Little did
anyone dream that another Englishman, very unlike Markham, living in South America, was soon to change the
whole future of cinchona in Java. How he did so comprises the most fortuitous and accidental incident in the
history of quinine. His name was Charles Ledger.

He had lived for years at Puno, Peru, on the shore of
Lake Titicaca which divides Peru and Bolivia. Living
within reasonable distance of the region that always had

provided the best barks, he not only traded in them, but got to know where some of the best quinine-yielding trees were to be found.

He also knew of the Markham expedition, but circumstances prevented his joining it, which was unfortunate for Markham, for Ledger knew far more about *Cinchona* than the leader of the ill-starred British venture.

Ledger for years had an intelligent Indian servant, Manuel Incra Mamani, well versed in forest lore and perfectly familiar with the best gathering ground for cinchona bark. Accordingly, Ledger sent Manuel to the headwaters of the Rio Beni, a tributary of the Upper Amazon in nearby Bolivia. Years before, Ledger had visited this site and remembered that the bark was of exceptional richness. Manuel did not return for some years, giving as an excuse that the seeds Ledger had asked him to gather failed to mature—the region was so high that frosts prevented seed setting. The excuse may be flimsy, but he did finally arrive at Puno with fourteen pounds of seed of what was presumably *Cinchona calisaya*. This had for years been the favorite species for high quinine yield.

Considering their ultimate value, which no one suspected, these seeds have a fantastic history. For they were to settle once for all who was to supply the world with quinine—the British or the Dutch.

Ledger sent them to his brother George in London with instructions to offer them to the British government for their plantations in British India. The English declined to have anything to do with them. Knowing that the seeds would not indefinitely retain their germinating power, George Ledger then offered the lot to the Dutch govern-

The *Cinchona* region in the Yungas of Bolivia, near Chulumani. Photograph by the author at Chulumani, Bolivia, May 17, 1944.

ment for their Java plantations. The Netherlands government bought one pound for one hundred francs with a promise of further payment if the seed germinated. Soon after they paid an additional sum of £24.

George Ledger returned to England with the thirteen re-

JAIL AT COROICO, BOLIVIA

Manuel Incra Mamani, the Indian servant of Charles Ledger, died here from a beating and exposure, after gathering the seeds which ultimately provided Java with *Cinchona ledgeriana*. Redrawn from a photograph by the author, at Coroico, Bolivia, May 26, 1944.

maining pounds of seed and literally hawked them about the streets of London. Finally, he induced a Mr. Money, a cinchona planter home from India on vacation, to purchase the lot. Money returned to India with his purchase, but on the way became skeptical of their value. Upon his arrival in India, he induced the British Indian Cinchona

[47]

Plantation to exchange the Ledger seed for a like amount of *Cinchona succirubra,* a species then very popular in India. Thus it finally worked out that the seeds gathered by Manuel in far off Bolivia were planted by the British Indian Government, just as Charles Ledger had wished.

Neither he nor the government knew of the existence of some pixy which then, and still, baffles cinchona culture in British India. At any rate the Ledger seed either failed to germinate, or those that did never reached productive capacity. No misfortune in the whole history of cinchona culture in India was so disastrous to the British. The country has the highest incidence of malaria in the world, and ever since the Ledger fiasco the government has been obliged to grow the inferior varieties sent there by the Markham expedition.

In view of what has happened since, the receipt of the single remaining pound of Ledger seed in Java, in December 1865, was a dramatic event. But no one suspected it; least of all no one dreamed that it was ultimately to mean the end of all their own failures, of which just then they were acutely conscious.

What happened to Charles Ledger's seed comprises the rest of the story of *Cinchona* in Java. However, before we leave this English benefactor of a Dutch enterprise, his subsequent history furnishes a curious contrast. The Dutch paid him at first a hundred francs, then a subsequent payment of £24.

Some time after this, the Dutch sent living plants from the Ledger seeds to the British for their Madras plantation. Markham, who still advised the British on *Cinchona* in India, well knew that this gift might still retrieve their original failure, and applied to the government of India for a grant of £200 to Ledger. It was refused. He made another appeal "for some slight recognition of Mr. Ledger's services. My request was again refused." At that moment the British were spending thousands of pounds in cultivating the wrong tree.

The Dutch, when the value of Ledger's seeds became apparent, paid him an additional sum of 1200 guilders in 1880. In January 1895, after Ledger's retirement to Australia, the Dutch paid him an annual salary of 1200 guilders.

The single pound of Ledger seed, bought by the Dutch, was received by K. W. van Gorkom, who had succeeded Hasskarl and F. W. Junghuhn as director of the Government Cinchona Estate in Java. A considerable part of the seed had spoiled, but the rest was carefully planted and about 20 thousand germinated. Of these, 12 thousand were set out in a nursery bed the following year. No one had the faintest idea that this routine procedure, which had been repeated scores of times, was fraught with anything in particular. It was just another shipment of South American seed, none of which, so far, had been anything but a relatively costly failure.

To the eyes of a geneticist, no setting could be worse for these new seedlings of *Cinchona ledgeriana,* as the Ledger plants were subsequently christened. Java had hundreds of thousands of *Cinchona* trees, many of them flowering and fruiting and none of them of much value. *Cinchona* is, in any case, a heterostyled genus much given to hybridizing. Many "species" and "varieties" were of dubious genetic validity, and they had come from collec-

[49]

tors who gathered their seed all over the Andes. It was thus to a highly mongrelized plant society that *C. ledgeriana* was first introduced. Why and how it became the world source of quinine seems today all but miraculous.

The difficulty of standardizing a variety or strain of *Cinchona* is far greater than in most other plants, just because the genus is heterostylous—a botanical term that needs brief definition to understand the problem that faced the Dutch. Most plants have pistils (or styles) of similar length. Some have pistils of two lengths, but *Cinchona* is heterostylous and happens to have styles of three lengths. Not many plants have this characteristic, but common examples are the purple loosestrife (*Lythrum Salicaria*) and the primrose (*Primula vera*) of Europe.

Charles Darwin, about the time that *Cinchona ledgeriana* arrived in Java, was the first scientist to point out the sexual significance of heterostylous plants. Without following Darwin too far among the intricacies of technical botany, it is enough for us that he proved the difference in the length of pistils (styles) was a device of nature to prevent self-pollination and ensure cross-pollination. Insects are the carriers of the pollen from flower to flower, and the heterostyly of *Cinchona* makes it normally impossible to keep progeny pure.

With many other "species" and "varieties" of *Cinchona* scattered all over western Java, the chances of foreign pollen polluting the population of *Cinchona ledgeriana* was thus not only likely but certain. Such a catastrophe could not happen, of course, until the Ledger seedlings were old enough to flower. Some varieties, especially when the cultural conditions are poor, may flower prematurely,

[50]

even as early as the fourth or fifth year. It's a bad sign and such trees were destroyed by the thousands when the Dutch realized its significance. But no one knew just when *C. ledgeriana* would flower, or whether the tree was worth anything or not.

To determine its value the officials of the government Cinchona Estate at Tjinjiroean, where the Ledger seedlings were growing, were fortunate in securing the services of J. C. B. Moens. He was a young chemist from Holland who went to Java in 1872 for the express purpose of determining the exact alkaloidal content of the different barks. He made thousands of analyses, and it was due to him that the Dutch ultimately destroyed hundreds of thousands of low-yield trees. Until the Ledger seedlings proved their worth, these miscellaneous "species" and "varieties" were the only source of quinine from the Java plantings, in spite of the fact that their yield of quinine sulfate was not much, if any, greater than the barks found in South America today.

Very carefully, and without destroying a single Ledger seedling, Moens removed a piece of bark from a few trees for testing. He expected nothing greater than had been found in all the other species. It is not difficult to imagine his surprise when, in 1872, he made this first test of *Cinchona ledgeriana,* and got results that made it apparent that this "species" was itself a complex of different strains varying widely in alkaloidal content. It was also likely, as was ultimately determined to be the fact, that the same individual tree produced varying amounts as it grew older, and very little while still a sapling. His results are best shown in tabular form:

[51]

Year Examined	Number of Trees Examined	Maximum Content of Quinine Sulfate
1872	7	8.15%
1873	20	10.90%
1874	29	11.68%
1875	14	10.72%
1876	52	13.25%
1877	19	12.31%
1878	54	10.67%

These figures would have thrown a less cautious people than the Dutch into an orgy of *Cinchona* speculation. But perhaps they had learned a lesson from the tulip craze in Holland when the government was forced to stop a riot of speculation after a single bulb sold for ten thousand dollars in 1630. At any rate Moens and his chief, van Gorkom, realized that these spectacular quinine figures did not solve the *Cinchona* problem. Only the maximum yields are given above, but they well knew that from some of the trees tested the yields were as low as .65%, 1.67% and 3.22%. Even the latter, however, were higher than the old series of trees from Hasskarl, Schuhkraft and the rest. In commenting on Moens's analyses, van Gorkom writes: "Before this (Ledger) kind was known in Java, it was considered that American barks with 3% quinine were of very good quality; barks with more than 5% were held to be exceptionally fine." That was written in 1881, but it applies with equal truth today, to all but a negligible fraction of barks from Bolivia which are higher in quinine than those from any other South American country.

Subsequent analyses by Moens provided van Gorkom

with a clear picture of just what to expect from the total population of *C. ledgeriana,* all of which was derived from the original lot of Ledger seed. Upon the basis of other analyses by Moens, van Gorkom was faced with a decision of what to do with the relatively worthless trees left from the collections of Hasskarl and Junghuhn, both of whom had preceded him as director of the Government Cinchona Estate. This was no mean feat, for just after the first analyses of *C. ledgeriana* the trees of other species, actually planted in permanent locations, were as follows:

Cinchona calisaya	1,235,000
Cinchona succirubra	179,000
Cinchona officinalis	262,000
Cinchona lancifolia	27,000
Cinchona micrantha	1,030
Total	1,704,030

All of these, except *C. succirubra,* have long since disappeared from Java, but they posed a serious problem to van Gorkom for two reasons: The first was that many of them grew on mountain slopes which Junghuhn had rightly demonstrated were best for *Cinchona* culture. The other, and potentially far more dangerous fact was that these ultimately discarded species would pollute the best of the Ledger trees and van Gorkom well understood this hazard. He was determined to preserve the sexual purity of *C. ledgeriana* at all costs, and his solution turned out to be simplicity itself.

Carefully selecting the highest yielding Ledger trees,

he segregated these into different groups, depending not only upon yield but hardiness, thriftiness, amount and thickness of bark, admixture of other alkaloids, ease of transplanting, and other horticultural peculiarities he thought important. For each group he cleared a small area of virgin forest, too far from other *Cinchona* plantations, and from each other, to permit the flight of bees or other insects to cross pollinate the selected stock. With his precious young Ledger trees safely protected, one might suppose he could quietly sit back and await developments.

But the next few years were scarcely a life of ease. What should be done with the enormous stock of relatively worthless trees representing a huge investment? How could he be sure that the remaining Ledger trees, which had not been isolated, would be safe from other pollen pollution—supposing some of them developed desirable qualities as yet unsuspected? To guard against the latter contingency, thousands of trees surrounding the main Ledger plantation were annually de-flowered, so that there was little or no pollen pollution. The extent of such an operation will perhaps only be appreciated by a geneticist.

Getting rid of the early failures was a more difficult matter. Until *C. ledgeriana* came into full production, a matter of some years hence, the miscellaneous species of *Cinchona* in Java were the only source of Dutch quinine. Gradually, over a period of years, the Netherlands Indies Government issued decrees forbidding the propagation of these trees. Relying partly upon destruction and partly upon regular bark harvesting, the effect of these orders was to eliminate all *Cinchona* from Java but *C. ledgeriana*, *C. succirubra*, and the hybrids. The retention of the former was, of course, obvious, for it was then and has since remained, the highest quinine yielding species in the world. *Cinchona succirubra*, at first retained for purely a chemical reason, is now also kept for a practical horticultural operation, the significance of which is inherent in modern *Cinchona* culture.

Cinchona ledgeriana, while extraordinarily high in quinine production, is low in its yield of quinidine, cinchonine and cinchonidine. This is at once an advantage and a disadvantage. In extracting quinine sulfate from the bark, it is of considerable benefit if the process is not complicated by the presence of other alkaloids. *C. ledgeriana* meets that specification better than any other tree in the genus.

There is, however, and always has been, a demand for these other alkaloids of *Cinchona* and the virtue of *C. succirubra*, among its many other advantages, is that, while very low in quinine, it is high in quinidine, cinchonine and cinchonidine. With these two species in real production, the Dutch were in the position of being able to supply all the cinchona alkaloids. It still took many years to reach this enviable position. But at last, after many failures, much criticism of the Government Cinchona Estate as "the expensive folly," and years of work by Moens and van Gorkom, the attempt to grow *Cinchona* in Java appeared to be on the road to success.

The Dutch were, however, still faced with a rather serious hazard, for *Cinchona ledgeriana* turned out to be a horticulturally difficult tree to grow, especially those strains of it that showed exceptionally high quinine yields. It was quite unlike the robust, easily-grown *C. succirubra*

[55]

which flourished then in Java as it does today all over Guatemala to which it was taken from Ceylon in 1873. This tree, yielding the so-called red bark, is no more difficult to grow in any tropical region than growing willows along a stream in the temperate zone. But *C. ledgeriana,* the present world source of quinine, is an entirely different matter. The final solution of this difficulty brings us to modern culture methods in Java.

6 CINCHONA IN JAVA:
   THE FINAL GOAL

C INCHONA culture in Java would never have become a
   success if the original lot of well isolated Ledger
trees had been left in the safe security of their forest clearings. It was the business of the Director of the Government
Cinchona Estate to propagate them, demonstrate what was
needed to make their culture a success, and finally offer
propagating material to the private planters. For it soon
became obvious that while the Netherlands Indies Government would have to continue, at a loss, all the necessary
experimental work, quinine production must ultimately
be in private hands—just as the introduction of tung was
first a government enterprise, but is now a private one in
the United States.

Private planters in Java (mostly tea and coffee growers)
had long looked askance at *Cinchona* culture. Until the
analyses of Moens', there was every justification for their
skepticism, but interest gradually grew, especially when a
few samples of Ledger bark fetched four times the price

[57]

of any other variety at the Amsterdam auction of June 1875. The planters showed even more interest when it became clear that the "expensive folly" of the Government Cinchona Estate was actually managed by van Gorkom and his chemist Moens, with quite extraordinary care and foresight. It has been so ever since, under a series of exceptionally able scientists among whom may be mentioned Romunde, Groothoff, van Leersum, Kerbosch and the present director, M. A. van Roggen.

Interest led to inquiry—just what sort of a tree was *Cinchona ledgeriana,* what were its climatic and soil requirements, how did one harvest it and how long must one wait for that harvest? These were pertinent questions in 1875, just as they are today, and lack of precise answers would have doomed cinchona culture in Java just as it has in more than twenty other attempts—of which more later.

Cinchona ledgeriana is a medium sized tree belonging to the family Rubiaceae, a group of plants with which Java was already familiar. It contains besides *Cinchona,* coffee, ipecac, the fragrant *Gardenia* and the gorgeous *Ixora,* a shrub planted all over Java for its scarlet flowers. Excepting only coffee, none of these is of anything like the importance of *C. ledgeriana.*

This is botanically related to *C. calisaya* of Bolivia, and to distinguish it from that species it was first christened *C. calisaya* var. *ledgeriana.* But its importance swept away some uncertainty as to its true varietal status, and Howard, a British quinologist, decided it should stand on its own feet and proclaimed it a true species—quite appropriately giving it the name of *C. ledgeriana.* This was published in the *Gardeners' Chronicle* of London in 1879

Collecting the seed capsules. These are carefully sorted into linen bags and taken to a darkened room for ultimate harvesting of the seed.

(page 457) and the tree has been so called ever since, notwithstanding protests from botanical purists.

It reaches a height of about 30 feet in fourteen years, in Java, with a diameter of about 8 inches. At 45 years it may well be 75-80 feet with a trunk diameter of 14-16 inches. If grown in the open, which scarcely ever happens, it has ascending branches and a pyramidal or conical crown, while the trunk is fairly straight and covered with a roughish, brown bark which is apt to be obscured by a film of grayish-green lichens.

Its opposite leaves have no marginal teeth, and are perfectly smooth, the blade being more or less elliptic and with usually nine pairs of principal veins, besides the midrib. One very characteristic feature is that where each lateral vein joins the midrib there is a distinct but slight pit (scrobiculate). On young twigs the leaf blade may be as much as 8–9 inches long, while on mature, but non-flowering twigs it will average $3\frac{1}{2}$–6 inches. On the flowering branches the leaves are somewhat shorter.

The lilac-like flower cluster is erect or nodding, sometimes almost feathery, and deliciously scented. Each flower is about $\frac{1}{2}$ inch long, short-stalked, trumpet-shaped, 5-lobed and always cream colored (never red or pinkish). The inside of the flower is rather densely woolly and the lobes are fringed with fine hairs (ciliate.) As mentioned earlier, the plant is heterostylous and its flowers are followed by a dry fruit (capsule) usually not over $\frac{1}{2}$ inch long, which always splits from the bottom upward, thus releasing the seeds.

The latter are extraordinarily minute, and are very narrowly winged (to be seen only under a lens). Some idea of their size may be gathered from the fact that a single ounce of seed would contain approximately 98 thousand (about 3500 seeds per gram).

PREFERRED HABITAT

Most species of *Cinchona* are mountain lovers and *C. ledgeriana* is no exception, but unlike some sorts it does not favor extreme elevations. After years of trial and error, the preferred elevations for its best growth in Java are between 3,000 and 7,000 feet, just south of the equator. Below this it will grow quickly for the first few years, but gradually dies out, while in elevations above its preferred limit, its growth is very slow and it has a tendency to become a mere shrub.

An adequate rainfall is essential and provided certain soil conditions are right, this may easily be as high as 125 inches per year. In some favored locations there is somewhat more than this. Below an annual rainfall of 90 inches the tree will not thrive. Of even more importance than the amount of rainfall is its distribution. There must be no dry season of more than a month's duration, and it is this factor that makes *Cinchona* culture in much of Central and South America a hazardous undertaking. Much of the tropical American region which might otherwise be fit for at least a trial of *Cinchona,* is invalidated by a dry season (November to April), far too long for the requirements of the best culture. In Java no cinchona region has a dry season of more than one month, and even this is considered troublesome, especially for new, young plants.

The temperature range for Ledger trees is also an im-

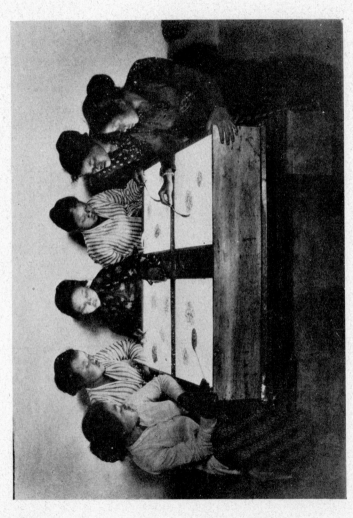

Seeds are selected in a darkened room. Upon sheets of ground glass, illuminated from below, these Javanese girls can detect those with an imperfect embryo.

portant factor. Day temperatures may range from 53°–86° F., and those at night from 46°–59°. Old trees will occasionally stand a little, but not repeated frosts, while all young trees are killed outright by frost. Such temperatures scarcely suggest the tropics, but midday heat coupled with much moisture make most cinchona plantations rather uncomfortably humid. In Bolivia mists and rainfall make the original home of Ledger's seed what some picturesque writers have called a "green hell." "Green Mansions" is a better term.

When Ledger trees were first set out it was possible to plant them in rich forest humus on freshly cleared land, which the tree certainly prefers. This, in a region so densely populated as Java, is no longer possible, and it became necessary to study soil conditions that were second best. These are the soils of volcanic origin, mostly on the northern slopes of the mountains in the Preanger Regency of western Java, of which Bandoeng is the chief town. Some people have called it the quinine capital of the world. The preferred, indeed the essential feature of the soil is that it must be reasonably porous, not only to permit the copious rainfall to percolate down, but to allow the tap-root of the tree its necessary depth. No region with a layer of hard-pan is ever chosen for cinchona culture.

In a region so mountainous as Java, it is next to impossible to find flat or gently sloping land, and this has led to an elaborate series of terraces upon which the trees are planted. Without such terraces, erosion would wash all the best soil into the valleys and cinchona culture would be impossible. The construction of these, as we shall see later, is a costly, difficult, and rather skillful undertaking.

If any of these conditions is lacking, *Cinchona* behaves as do most other plants. With everything to its liking, *C. ledgeriana* ought not to come into flower before the eighth or tenth year. Premature flowering used to plague the Dutch in Java, and it exists today in many Latin American plantations, but the Dutch destroyed such plants and looked elsewhere for just the right conditions to prevent early flowering. One of these, especially in young plantations, is relative freedom from wind. This is not always easy to provide, but it avoids the conditions that one can see today in some cinchona plantations in Latin America, where young windswept trees rush into premature bloom as though in protest against those who doomed them from the start.

*　　*　　*　　*　　*

In 1877 the Netherlands Indies Cinchona Estate was ready to permit private planters to begin cinchona culture in earnest. It was just about 12 years after the arrival of the Ledger seed, and they were fruitful in experience. Perhaps it is safe to say that if the government officials had done anything different from what they proposed there would be no cinchona culture in Java today.

It takes caution, restraint, and much patient skill to build for the future instead of reaping a quick profit. The extraordinary quinine yield of the first Ledger trees could easily have tempted a less conservative group, particularly in view of much criticism, to harvest that rich bark forthwith. Such a course would have satisfied those who saw nothing but folly in continuing, and were all for recouping some of the heavy expenses already incurred. It is needless now to recount the details of that struggle, but the final decision should be chalked up as a triumph of sanity.

Long before offering planting material to private growers, it was essential to make some scientific decisions of far reaching significance. In the last chapter we left the very finest of the Ledger trees in the safe security of sexual purity. They could not stay so indefinitely and the question of how to propagate them posed several questions. To have relied wholly on seed, would, in spite of isolation, have been a hazard that the officials were unwilling to face.

For the Dutch knew, perhaps without understanding the genetic reasons for it, that there was no guarantee that *all* the seedlings from a high yield tree would be equally high in quinine. To overcome this difficulty they made vegetative cuttings or grafting material of specially selected trees, and used these when mature and after many tests, as the final seed source. Such grafted trees, which were only to be used as a specially safeguarded seed supply, were like the original Ledger trees, put in forest clearings to prevent any possible pollen contamination. The government officials rightly guessed that all the necessary skill and care needed to maintain such a seed supply might be outside the competence of most private growers. And even today few private planters bother to have a seed garden which needs such expert care. They rely upon the Government Cinchona Estate which has kept up the supply ever since. It charges private planters from three to four dollars per gram for the best Ledger varieties, (there have been several hybrid strains developed) and this fact almost alone has maintained the high yield of Javan *Cinchona*.

[63]

Another feature of cinchona culture in which the private planters needed much instruction was the inability of *C. ledgeriana* to grow on its own roots, once virgin forest sites were exhausted. The trees either did not grow well, or their quinine content dropped off, whenever they were planted on land that had already grown a crop of *Cinchona*. This dilemma might well have stopped the culture forthwith, and the solution did not come from the officials of the Government Cinchona Estate. They had tried various methods of overcoming this difficulty, but the final solution was suggested by a nurseryman from Boskoop, Holland, a Mr. J. W. van Loon, who happened to be visiting Java.

He noticed the extremely thrifty growth of *Cinchona succirubra* in all sorts of situations and from the highest mountains nearly to sea level. *Cinchona succirubra* needs a bit of explanation. It came originally from the northern Andes through the Markham expedition, to British India. In the constant exchange of plants and ideas between the British and Dutch, *C. succirubra,* which is still widely grown in India, finally came to Java. As a source of quinine sulfate it is next to worthless, and the Dutch paid little attention to it beyond noting its vigor and its possible use as a source of alkaloids other than quinine.

But a practical nurseryman like van Loon saw in *C. succirubra* an answer to the question of what to do about the admitted difficulty of growing *C. ledgeriana* on its own roots. Why not try plate grafting—a procedure perfectly familiar to all nurserymen? It was tried and has been used ever since, so that it became necessary to grow thousands (ultimately millions) of *C. succirubra* to use as a stock upon which to graft cions of *C. ledgeriana.* Present

[64]

GRAFTING CINCHONA IN THE NURSERY

A skillful operator will complete about 400 in a day.

needs also require that a comparatively small acreage of *C. succirubra* is grown for harvesting its bark, which is rich in quinidine, cinchonine and cinchonidine. It is this that is called "pharmaceutical bark," for it is harvested in a special way and goes into some pharmaceutical products.

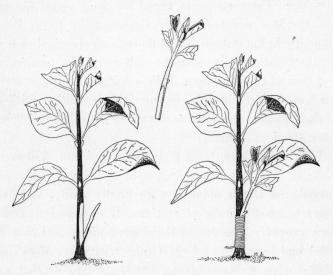

CINCHONA GRAFTING

At left the stock of *Cinchona succirubra*, prepared for grafting; in the center the cion of *C. ledgeriana*; at the right the completed job.

Ledger bark, harvested only for the manufacture of quinine sulfate, is thus generally known as "factory bark."

Botanical and horticultural experts were quick to question the solution of grafting a high-yield upon a low-yield tree. Technical terms, such as chimaera, graft-hybrid and others still more erudite, are thus sprinkled through the literature of *Cinchona*. The practical question was whether the high yield of *C. ledgeriana* would be lost when it was grafted upon *C. succirubra*, or whether the quinine content of *C. succirubra* would be increased by the draining away of quinine from the cion of *C. ledgeriana*. Thousands of chemical tests were made by the Dutch to settle this point. The controversy raged for many years and was perhaps best summed up by Groothoff in 1919. He is emphatic in the statement that there is no chemical change, in either direction, between the understock of *C. succirubra* and cion of *C. ledgeriana*. This is fortunate for successful cinchona culture in Java is based upon making millions of these grafts, a procedure requiring not a little skill in a moist tropical climate.

With a seed supply as pure as science and skill could make it, and with the technique of grafting already conquered, the Dutch planters were finally ready, and even eager to start private plantations. It is hoped that they were properly grateful to their government and that the latter had forgotten or forgiven the long years of ridicule heaped upon an undertaking that is perhaps without parallel in the history of tropical agriculture.

No tree, not even rubber, has ever had such a long history of patient, intelligent care bestowed upon it. And it should be remembered that many features of cinchona culture, too technical for inclusion here, have taken years to settle. Such a co-ordination of soil science, climatology, chemistry, genetics, forest ecology and just plain Dutch common sense, has scarcely ever been duplicated—if ever. Up to this point the government of the Netherlands Indies had spent much money, a good many years, without thought of profit, and quite simply to do what one of their

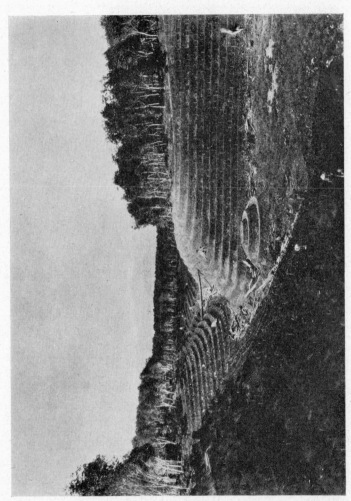

Terraces must be made to provide permanent planting sites.

Governors General had said originally: ". . . . to procure for the sick, the means of life. . . ."

We thus bid goodbye to the Indies Government, because from that day to this cinchona culture in Java has been almost wholly in the hands of more than a hundred private planters, who are well organized and do their job well enough to keep the world supplied with quinine. The government still keeps its Cinchona Estate, largely as an experiment station, for they still hope to perfect their technique. Up at Tjinjiroean there are still some of those magical trees from Charles Ledger's seed. Like old horses they are pastured out and seed is no longer collected from them, no doubt because the practical Dutch know that increasing age means waning quinine yield.

CINCHONA CULTURE

In planning a cinchona plantation it is to be assumed that the private grower knows the requirements of the two species involved and that he is ready to provide them with their rather specialized needs. Of these the soil must be his first consideration. If, as usually happens, it is on a rather steep slope, it must be terraced as shown in the illustration. These are made so that the planting surface is nearly flat while the different levels look much like immense stepping stones up the face of the mountain. In making such terraces it is usually impossible to preserve what forest humus may be left on the site, but it is essential that the soil on each terrace be friable enough to permit percolation so that no standing water is left in them—a condition that *C. ledgeriana* will not tolerate. The making

[67]

of these terraces is an engineering job of some complexity in a mountainous terrain, for they must be so constructed that they prevent erosion, stimulate percolation, and prevent accumulation of stagnant water.

The grower must also provide himself with adequately shaded seed beds, a nursery to take care of young seedlings and other horticultural necessities. Especially there must be good compost heaps of fine woods soil or

A Javanese shelter for seed beds, so constructed as to regulate the light and prevent too violent air currents.

crushed humus, because for seeds so fine it is essential to provide a specially prepared seed bed. This must be shaded with lath or cheese cloth, and all draught or wind kept out of the bed for several weeks. So minute are the seeds that watering must be done with the finest, misty spray. Too much water will inevitably lead to the dreaded "damping-off"—a microscopic fungus disease so destructive that it may kill hundreds of seedlings in a single day. In the young stages of cinchona culture no operation is so carefully watched as watering.

Seed sowing requires much care, for they average about 3,500 to the gram and hence require delicate handling.

The seeds are scattered evenly on finely ground humus or woods soil, and with proper care should germinate 12-14 days after planting. Slow germination means poor seed or failure to provide proper conditions, and it is usually the latter because the Government Cinchona Estate selects its seeds with meticulous care. The seedlings germinate profusely (80-90%) so that the young seedlings are usually so densely crowded that they cannot stay in the seed bed more than a few months. At four months they may well be 2-3½ inches high and must then be transplanted and re-spaced.

It is scarcely worth while to follow their course for the next 14-18 months. Successively they are permitted more light, transferred to nursery beds and are finally, about two years from seeding, "hardened off" and ready to be put in the permanent plantation. At this time they should be 18-24 inches high.

In the meantime the grower has seen to it that thrifty young plants of *C. succirubra* have been set out on the sites which are to be ultimately covered with *C. ledgeriana*. The *C. succirubra* plants are at this time about as thick as a lead pencil and 18-24 inches high. On to these "whips" of *C. succirubra* the cions of *C. ledgeriana* are inserted by plate grafting, a skillful operator making about 400 grafts per day. Sometimes these grafts are made in the nursery for ultimate removal to permanent sites.

The operation is then complete and beyond weeding (a serious business in the humid tropics), and an occasional cover crop of legumes for soil enrichment, the grower can sit back and wait for his harvest. When to expect that has been the cause of many headaches and some scientific controversy.

The trees are usually planted at four foot intervals, which means 2722 trees per acre. This is far too crowded for permanent growth. On the other hand *C. ledgeriana* does not develop its true quinine content until after the fourth or fifth year. At some time about this period, the cautious planter will then thin out part of his trees, cutting them at the ground level, thus abandoning the roots of *C. succirubra* upon which they were grafted. Although the bark of the abandoned roots would yield some alkaloid, and hence a little income, he does not dare risk disturbing the roots of the remaining trees which are to form his permanent plantation.

The cut tops of the harvested *C. ledgeriana* which, naturally, as young saplings, have rather thin bark, do not yield much quinine, but it is the grower's first income even if it is far from being a profit. For the next few years he may thin out occasional diseased or crippled trees, but never enough to prevent what the foresters call a closed canopy. This obviates future weeding, and it also appears to control a disease that is apt to attack trees grown with an open canopy.

His real harvest does not come until 15-18 years from planting time. The tree is then in full vigor, nearly at its peak of quinine content, and has reached a size and thickness of bark to make it most profitable for cutting. The tree, roots and all, is removed from the site and is ready for the final stages of quinine production. Such wholesale destruction of trees that take so long to grow and need so much care, led to many suggestions for different meth-

Drying frames for bark. These can be closed at night to prevent re-absorption of evening mist or dew.

ods of bark harvesting. Three different schemes, all orig-
inating in India, were tried by the Dutch, often on thousands of trees, but all have been abandoned for the present plan of completely clearing off the trees. The British
methods have only historical or academic interest today.
One involved coppicing the whole plantation and harvesting the stump suckers. Another was the "mossing" method
which involved cutting only long strips of bark from living
trees and covering the stripped areas with moss, while wait-
ing for bark renewal. The third method was scraping off
thin parings or shavings of outer bark which was supposed
not to injure the living tree. Scientifically and economically, all these were failures.

The planter, however, who has just cleared his land of
trees that are 15-18 years old, is presented with far from
an academic problem. Merely to grow one crop, as farmers
grow wheat, would in the case of the Java cinchona
planter, leave him with nothing but a single bark harvest
each 15-18 years. In this respect his neighbor who grows
rubber, tea or coffee, is far better off, for each of them
yields an annual crop from the same plants which may
go on bearing for years.

It is this fact, little understood by the public, which
makes cinchona growers keep a constant succession of
plants from seed bed, nursery, hardening off grounds and
permanent plantations. They plant today for 16 years
hence, next year for 17 years hence and so on. There must
be no gaps in the sequence, for it might well mean that
some years later when those trees *should* have been harvested, there would be no quinine. Actually, such a contingency is not likely to happen, for the commercial plan-

tations, under the guidance of the Government Cinchona Estate, are very well managed.

The trees of harvested *C. ledgeriana* are cut up into short logs and the bark stripped from them by beating with wooden mallets. Often, bone knives help to loosen it from the logs—steel knives are taboo. At this stage, the bark

Sun drying of the bark is sometimes done in these trays that are rolled under cover at night for protection from rain or dew.

contains about 70% of water. It is then put in the sun for a few days which leaves it with approximately 13% of water. The rest of the water must be driven off by artificial heat, and all the larger plantations are provided with special drying furnaces for this purpose. In these the temperature must not exceed 175°F. The completely dried bark, which has been pulverized or broken into small chips, is then ready for packing and shipment. This is the "fac-

[72]

A mature plantation of Javanese *Cinchona* with the highest content of quinine sulfate found in the world.

tory" bark of commerce, ready for the extraction of quinine, of which it contains more than any other bark in the world. The bark from the roots which, of course, are all *C. succirubra* is separated from the bark of the trunk and larger branches. It is used for the extraction of alkaloids other than quinine.

Some plantations, but only a few, grow a little *C. succirubra* on its own roots for its bark, as all of them must grow it for grafting stock. It yields the so-called "pharmaceutical" bark which is dried in a different way from *C. ledgeriana*. Pharmaceutical bark, while it contains quinidine, cinchonine, and cinchonidine, is sold also for its looks. Such bark is harvested in strips which, either naturally or by inducement, dry in rolls or quills. It requires more careful handling because dried bark is brittle and the quills are then easily broken. This industry represents less than 6% of modern cinchona culture, basically because the yield of quinine is so low. At the moment (1944), this and similarly low yield varieties are practically the only cinchona barks coming from tropical America to the United States, where some of it is being made into quinine, but most of it is used to make totaquina.

ECONOMIC CONSIDERATIONS

In August 1943, the Bureau of Foreign Commerce of the United States Department of Commerce announced that two million bushels of wheat had just been burned in the Argentine because the growers could find no market for it. Everyone remembers the burning of coffee in Brazil, of wheat in Kansas, the rooting out of rubber trees in

Malaya, and the slaughter of unwanted pigs in the United States. Some of these economic absurdities were born during the great depression, but their real cause came from deeper roots. These, bluntly, were the normal greed of the planters, the consequent overproduction and the inevitable collapse of the markets.

Precisely the same thing happened to the Java cinchona growers some time after the Netherlands Indies Government withdrew. There was a perfectly normal rush to grow *Cinchona*, and far too much was planted. The abandoned plantations of Ceylon, which never recovered from the Markham fiasco, were stripped of bark and this was also thrown on the market. It was a situation that inevitably depressed the price of bark to a point where the planters faced ruin. The whole industry was on the verge of extinction and the desperate planters formed an association for their own protection. One of their remedies was to petition the government for the right to erect their own quinine factory at Bandoeng. This was done and at least the growers were assured of a market for some of their bark at a reasonable profit. Ultimately, by an arrangement between the European manufacturers, the Bandoeng factory and the association of planters, the whole industry was put upon a sound financial footing.

That agreement has not escaped the censure of those who believe that there is something inherently wicked in competence and success especially if it is followed by co-ordinated production. They overlook also that its working, over the years, has not only prevented the destruction of an essential industry, but provided the world with the chief source of quinine in existence. Some, including members of the Peoples' Council (the legislative body of the Netherlands Indies at Batavia), have stated that the price of quinine is too high. To thoroughly investigate the latter point, the People's Council appointed a committee in 1936. After several months' work, their report made clear one inescapable fact regarding the whole industry.

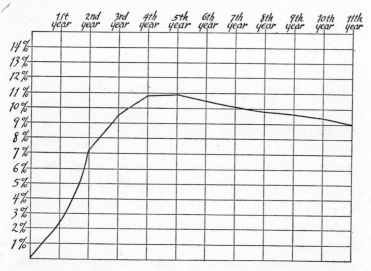

Tree age and yield of quinine sulfate. At the left the percentage of quinine in dried bark of *Cinchona ledgeriana* as grown in Java.

There is no economic magic by which a planter can be coaxed or forced to grow *Cinchona*, if in 15-18 years he is not assured of a reasonable price for his bark. Failing that assurance he will turn his land over to tea or coffee which require conditions not very different from *Cinchona*, and yield an annual crop without yearly re-planting. The Council also pointed out the calamity that would arise if no quinine were available due to well meant interference.

[75]

And finally, the Council, many of whom were rather hostile to the whole cinchona industry, made no serious recommendations for changing the present arrangement.

The report of the Committee is a model of objective reasoning based on first-hand study of the problem on the spot. At first they had no doubt been influenced by criticism of the cinchona industry, some of it informed, but much of it being founded upon insufficient knowledge of an admittedly difficult situation.

Omitting some purely technical details of interest only to trained horticulturists, the main points of the summary of the Cinchona Committee are worth recording: (1) The existing collaboration between bark producers and quinine manufacturers should be maintained. (2) A new Cinchona Agreement should be concluded for a definite period of at least ten years. (3) The price of quinine is not too high. It was their opinion that, only by the rigid application of the Cinchona Agreement could the industry be kept at its present efficiency.

That agreement protects the planters from the manufacturers, and the latter from the planters. Incidentally, it protects the public from the danger that quinine would be as scarce as ambergris. As to price, the cost of a five-day quinine treatment of malaria is less than the admission to one good movie. And it is far cheaper to treat malaria with quinine than pneumonia with the sulfa drugs. That economically impoverished populations cannot afford quinine is a truism. Neither can they buy many other things considered necessary. The amelioration of such economic conditions is beyond the scope of this book and it is mentioned here only because the issue is sometimes confused. There is much room for improvement among all impoverished people, but their inability to buy quinine is scarcely a valid criticism of that industry, and the Peoples' Council did not fall into this obvious error.

What the solution will be in a postwar world it is impossible to guess. Actually, the Cinchona Agreement as adopted by the Dutch just after the turn of the century, is the precursor of many others. Some, like the rubber and sugar agreements, have had their periods of stress, not unmixed with failure. Others, such as the coffee agreement entered into by the United States and the tropical American coffee growers, are patterned after the Dutch intent to protect the planters.

Some critics of *Cinchona* in Java, mostly quite ignorant of the facts, have accused the Dutch of trying to prevent anyone else from starting quinine plantations. Some planters in Java unquestionably wish the charge were true. With much labor and capital invested in their plantations, they can scarcely be blamed if they want cinchona culture restricted to Java. That perfectly normal reaction, however, is not shared by the Netherlands Indies Government.

It has already been noted that plants of *C. ledgeriana* were sent from Java to Madras, as part of an exchange of material which has gone on for many years between the Dutch and the British. More recently, quantities of seed were frequently given or sold by the Cinchona Estate to the U. S. Department of Agriculture. A partial record of gifts or sales of seeds furnished by the Netherlands Indies Cinchona Estate is as follows:

Australia	Mexico
New Caledonia	Brazil
Hawaii	Jamaica
Fiji Islands	Trinidad
Berlin Botanical Garden	Martinique
Vilmorin & Andrieux, Paris	California
German East Africa	Japan
(Tanganyika)	Federated Malay States
Madagascar	Sao Thomé
Belgian Congo	Reunion
Annam	Cochin China
U. S. Department of Agriculture	British India

There were many other smaller shipments, mostly to private planters, and usually comprising a gram or two of seeds of *C. ledgeriana*. Those in the list above stretch over a long period beginning in 1869. Not one of these attempts to produce quinine has come within measurable distance of the Dutch effort. Most of them were complete failures, perhaps the only exception being British India. This is largely a governmental enterprise maintained at a loss because quinine in some form must be produced for a population more subject to malaria than any other. Quite recent attempts of the United States, in co-operation with certain Latin American Republics, are as yet too young for final appraisal, while plantations in the Philippines have yielded chiefly totaquina.

One of the most skillful horticulturists in the United States recently wrote of the combination of science and skill that is the basis for growing all plants. He speaks of it as "the green hand," and those that lack it may just as well turn to something else. It is not just a fanciful word, for it tries to embody a welding of pure science with the patient, almost tender care that your true plant lover showers upon his favorites. The Dutch proved the truth of that concept four hundred years ago when they took the tulip from Turkey to Holland and made that country the world center for bulbs. In view of the many failures, and the long record of cinchona futility, it is difficult to escape the assumption that perhaps the green hand, and a Dutch one, made *Cinchona* in Java what it is.*

* The recent synthesis of quinine by R. B. Woodward and W. E. Doering of Harvard University is a remarkable chemical triumph which has baffled science ever since the attempt by Perkin in England in 1856. It scarcely detracts from the brilliance of their discovery that synthetic quinine is still, and is likely to be for years, more of a scientific curiosity than a practical source of the drug. (See Woodward, R. B. & Doering, W. E. "Total Synthesis of Quinine." *Journ. Amer. Chem. Soc.*, 1944, 66:849, also an editorial in *The New England Journal of Medicine* for October 16, 1944, page 606.)

BIBLIOGRAPHY

~~~~~~

To merely quote the literature on *Cinchona* would fill a much bigger book than this one. In America the best collections will be found in the libraries of the Arnold Arboretum, the New York Botanical Garden, the United States Department of Agriculture and the Cinchona Products Institute in New York. Among these the following appear to be of chief significance, omitting all the older historical accounts, as well as popular magazine articles.

Acta Conventus Tertii de Tropicis Atque Malariae Morbis. Amsterdam, 1938. 2 vols. Volume 2 (Pars. II Acta Conventus Tertii de Malariae Morbis) contains papers by the leading malariologists. 601 pages.

AMERICAN ASSOCIATION FOR THE ADVANCEMENT OF SCIENCE. *Symposium on Human Malaria.* Washington: A.A.A.S., 1941. 398 pages.

BOYD, M. F. *An Introduction to Malariology.* Cambridge: Harvard University Press, 1930. 437 pages.

BURNS, W. "Cinchona Cultivation in the Netherlands Indies," *Indian Farming,* (1940), 1:311-317.

CARDENAS, M. "Estado Actual de la Quinologia Boliviana," *Contrib. Flora Boliviana,* Cochabamba, (1941), 11 pages.

CENABRE, A. L. "Cinchona Culture in the Philippines," *Rev. Filipina de Med.,* (1937), 28:123-134.

EVANS, G. "The Possibility of Extending Cinchona Cultivation in the British Empire," *Empire Journ. Exp. Agr.,* (1941), 9:111-124.

[80]

BIBLIOGRAPHY

FRONTOU, G. "La Culture du Quinquina dans la Region ouest de Java," *Bull. Econ. Indo-China*, (1927), **30**:545-586.

GORKOM, K. W. VAN. *A Handbook of Cinchona Culture*. Transl. by B. D. Jackson. Amsterdam, 1883. 292 pages.

——. "Cinchona in Java from 1872 to 1907," *Agr. Ledger*, Calcutta, (1912), **17**: 35-106.

GOVERNMENTS KINA ONDERNEMING. *Annual Reports*. Bandoeng, 1915-1931.

GOVERNMENT OF BENGAL. *Ann. Reports of the Government Cinchona Plantations*. Calcutta, (Over 65 annual reports, 1869-1938).

GROOTHOFF, A. *Rationeele Exploitatie van Kinaplantsoenen in Verband met de Factoren, Welke Invloed Hebben of de Kwantiteit en het Gehatte der Basten*. Haarlem, 1919. 88 pages.

——. *De Kinacultuur*. (3d ed.). Haarlem, 1925. 122 pages.

HACKETT, L. W. *Malaria in Europe*. London: Oxford University Press, 1937. 336 pages.

HAGGIS, A. W. "Fundamental Errors in the Early History of Cinchona," *Bull. Hist. Med.*, (1941), **10**:417-459 + 568-592.

HENRY, T. A. *The Plant Alkaloids* (3d. edition), Philadelphia, 1939. 689 pages.

HOWARD, B. F. *Some Notes on the Cinchona Industry*. London: Streatfield Memorial Lecture, 1931. 22 pages.

JUNGHUHN, F. W. *An Account of the Quinine Plantations in the Island of Java*. Transl. by W. T. Fraser. Madras, 1861. 53 pages.

KERBOSCH, M. *Cinchona Culture in Java: Its History and Development*. 1930. (See Missouri Botanical Garden).

——. "Some Notes on Cinchona Culture and the World Consumption of Quinine." *Bull. Colonial Inst. Amsterdam*, (1939), **3**:36-51.

KINA PROEFSTATION. Mededeeling. Nos. 1-9. Batavia and Buitenzorg. 1912-1925.

LA WALL, C. H. "The History of Quinine." *Am. Journ. Pharm.* Philadelphia, (Jan. 1932), pp. 23-43.

[81]

LEAGUE OF NATIONS. (Health Organization). *Enquiry into the Quinine Requirements of Malarial Countries and the World Prevalence of Malaria.* Geneva, 1932. 89 pages.

———. *The Treatment of Malaria.* Geneva, 1937. 558 pages.

———. "Report on Terminology in Malaria." *Bull. Health Organization,* Geneva, (1940), **9**:131-246.

LEERSUM, P. VAN. Cinchona. (Revision of the chapter "Cinchona Culture") in van Gorkom's *Oost-Indische Cultures.* Amsterdam, 1919. 114 pages.

LOTSY, J. P. *Localization of the Alkaloid in Cinchona calisaya ledgeriana and in Cinchona succirubra.* Batavia, 1898. 72 pages.

MARAÑON, J. & BARTLETT, H. H. "Cinchona Cultivation and the Production of Totaquina in the Philippines," *Nat. & Appl. Sci. Bull. Univ. Philipp,* (1941), **8**:111-187.

MARKHAM, C. R. *Peruvian Bark: a Popular Account of the Introduction of Cinchona Cultivation into British India.* London, 1880, 550 pages.

MEYER, G. *Beiträge zur Anatomie der auf Java Cultivierten Cinchonen.* Stuttgart, 1900. 33 pages.

MISSOURI BOTANICAL GARDEN. *Proceedings of the Celebration of the 300th Anniversary of the First Recognized Use of Cinchona.* St. Louis, 1930. 258 pages. (Contains articles by A. Hogstad, Jr., G. T. Moore, L. Suppan, E. Kremers, G. Dock, R. J. Terry, M. Kerbosch, W. L. Scoville, F. Rosengarten, T. Sollmann, and K. F. Maxcy).

MOENS, J. C. B. *De Kinacultuur in Azië.* Batavia, 1882. 393 pages.

MORRISON, B. Y. "Quinine from Seed," *Agr. in the Americas,* (1943), **3**: 131-133.

OWEN, T. C. *The Cinchona Planter's Manual.* Colombo, 1881. 203 pages.

PELLETIER, J. & CAVENTOU, J. *Analyse Chimique des Quinquina.* Paris, 1821. 88 pages.

PILLI, E. R. *80 Años de Quina en Guatemala: un Relato Historico del Cultivo de la Cinchona de 1860 a 1942.* Guatemala City, 1943. 67 pages.

BIBLIOGRAPHY

POPENOE, W. "Cinchona in Guatemala," *Trop. Agr.*, Trinidad, (1941), **18**:70-74.

RUSBY, H. H. "The genus *Cinchona* in Bolivia." *Bull. Torrey Bot. Club*, (1931), **58**:523-530.

———. *Jungle Memories.* New York, 1933. 388 pages.

SANDS, W. N. "Cinchona Industry in Java," *Malayan Agr. Journ.* (1922), **10**:65-86.

SAPPINGTON, J. *The Theory and Treatment of Fevers.* ARROW ROCK, Mo., 1844. 216 pages.

SOUBEIRAN, J. L. & DELONDRE, A. *De l'introduction et de l'acclimatation des Cinchonas dans les Indies Neerlandaises et dans les Indes Britanniques.* Paris, 1868. 165 pages.

TAYLOR, N. "Cinchona—quinine to you." *Fortune*, (1934), **9**: 76-86.

———. "Quinine: the Story of Cinchona," *Sci. Mo.*, July, (1943), 18 pages.

WELLCOME HISTORICAL MEDICAL MUSEUM. *Souvenir Cinchona Tercentenary Celebration.* London, 1930, 115 pages.

WILSON, A. & MIRCHANDANI, T. J. *Prospects of Cinchona Cultivation in India.* Delhi, (1939), 121 pages.

WOOTTON, A. C. *Chronicles of Pharmacy.* London, 1910. Vol. 1, 428 pages. Vol. 2, 332 pages.

INDEX

(Includes names of plants, places, etc. and of people, except those in
the bibliography)

INDEX